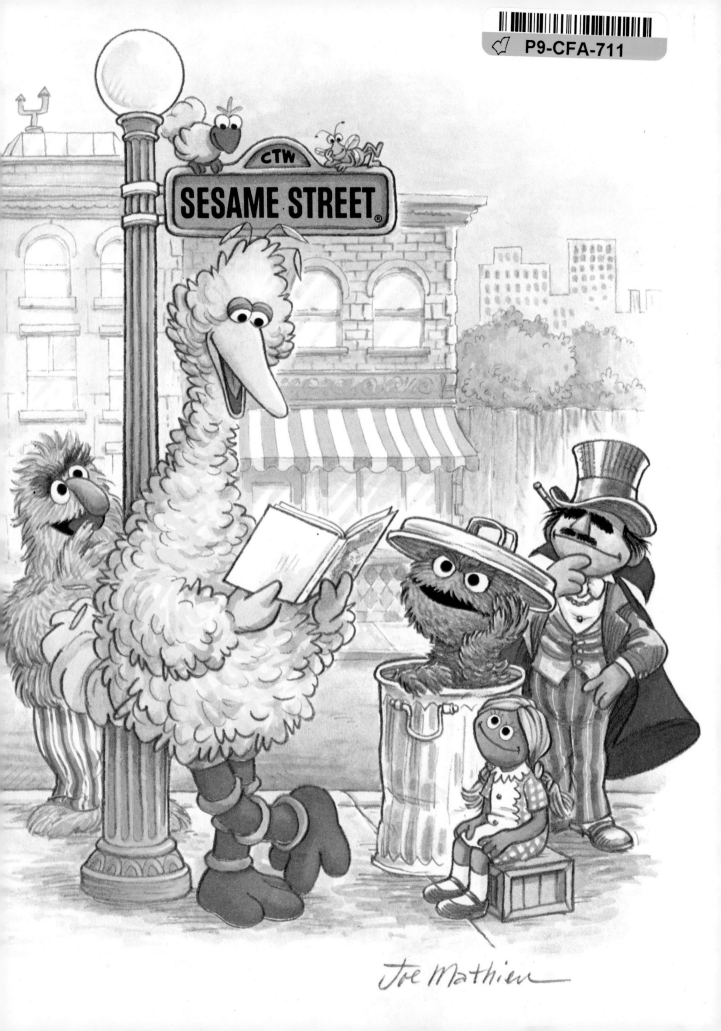

THE SESAME STREET® LIBRARY

With Jim Henson's Muppets

VOLUME 15

FEATURING
THE NUMBER
15

Children's Television Workshop/Funk & Wagnalls, Inc.

ILLUSTRATED BY:
Bill Basso
Richard Brown
Tom Cooke
Robert Dennis
Larry Di Fiori
Gerard Huerta
Jim Kinstrey/Whistl'n Dixie
Mary Schenck
Michael J. Smollin
Tabasco

PHOTOGRAPH BY:
Judy Ross

"The Case of the Mysterious Mud Puddle Monster"
written by David Korr

3 4 5 6 7 8 9 0

0-8343-0023-0-

The Count's Counting Page

Oh, look at all the steps!
I'm climbing all the steps!
I'm counting all the wonderful steps!
Oh, look at all the steps!
I think that I'll play in my attic today . . .
And then I can count all the steps on the way!

How many steps are there?

Grover's Trip

Hello. This is your old friend Grover. I went to visit my Auntie. She lives in California.

California is very far away. I had to take an airplane to get there. Here I am bundled up for my trip on the airplane.

It is cold and snowy where I live. But it is warm in California! Here I am after I got off the plane.

You know what they have in California? Oranges!

I also saw a Chinese New Year's parade. Look at the dragon!

California has lots of beaches. Here I am playing on the beach.

While I was here I made a new friend. She is from Mexico. She had a birthday party, and she invited me! Here I am trying to break the piñata.

I saw palm trees... and mountains ...

and a desert!

I had a wonderful trip! I hope you liked hearing about it!

1, 2 Green and Blue!

What numbers are green?
What numbers are blue?
What numbers are yellow?
What numbers are brown?
What numbers are orange?
What numbers are black?
What numbers are red?

6

11

2

13

1

10

15

3

8

7

There's more than one way ...

Snuffle-upagus is having a party. Big Bird wants to go to the party.
1. Take your finger and show Big Bird how to get to the party.
2. Take Big Bird past the fire station.
3. Now take a pencil. Show Big Bird the way.
4. Look again! There is another way to go! This time, take Big Bird past the library.
5. Draw a line from Big Bird to the library. Draw a line from the library to the party.
6. Can you show Big Bird another way to go to Snuffie's party?

Fire Dept.

It's Barkley!

Remembering
Look carefully at this picture.
Turn the page.

Mike Smollin

What's Missing?

The Case of the Mysterious Mud Puddle Monster

One day, Big Bird decided to take a walk around Sesame Street. He opened his door and stepped out— right into a mud puddle. "Oh, drat," he said. "Phooey." But it was too nice a day to fret, so he went on his way, forgetting all about the puddle.

Next he stopped at Mr. Hooper's store for a birdseed soda and an apple. Prairie Dawn was minding the store for Mr. Hooper, and Cookie Monster was also there, having a cookie sandwich. Big Bird drank his soda, ate his apple, and chatted for a while with his friends.

First he went to the home of Oscar the Grouch, who lived in a trash can and collected trash. Big Bird wanted to give him some old papers he had saved. Oscar said, "Swell, now leave me alone," and Big Bird left, happy that Oscar liked his present.

Then he remembered that Ernie and Bert had invited him to come see their new tablecloth, so he decided to visit them. After he had admired the tablecloth, which was covered with blue and white squares, he told Ernie and Bert how much he liked it, and set off for home.

When he got there, he saw Sherlock Hemlock, the world's greatest detective, looking through a magnifying glass at something on the ground.

"Hi, Mr. Hemlock," said Big Bird. "Are you looking for clues with your magnifying glass?"

"Indeed I am, Big Bird," said Sherlock Hemlock. "I, Sherlock Hemlock, the world's greatest detective, am investigating my newest case."

"Oh, boy!" said Big Bird. "What kind of case is it?"

"It's THE CASE OF THE MYSTERIOUS MUD PUDDLE MONSTER," answered Sherlock Hemlock.

"The Mud Puddle Monster!" said Big Bird, feeling just a little frightened. "What's a Mud Puddle Monster?"

"That," said Sherlock Hemlock, "is the mystery. I don't know what a Mud Puddle Monster is. But I'm going to find out, or I'm not Sherlock Hemlock, the world's greatest detective." Sherlock Hemlock pointed his finger at the ground. "I already have some clues," he said. "Look. These are footprints. And do you see where they start? They start right here, at this mud puddle. That means that whoever made these footprints came *out* of the mud puddle! Now, who else would come out of a mud puddle but a Mud Puddle Monster?"

"My goodness, you're clever, Mr. Hemlock," said Big Bird, bending over to look at the muddy footprints and the puddle. "Hmmm," he said thoughtfully. "That looks just like the mud puddle *I* stepped in a little while ago."

"Egad!" said Sherlock Hemlock. "Another clue. When you stepped in this mud puddle, you made the Mud Puddle Monster *mad*. That is why he came out of the puddle."

"He's mad? Do you mean he's mad at *me*?" asked Big Bird, feeling a little more frightened than before.

"Yes, indeed," said Sherlock Hemlock. "He's mad at you. He's also quite large."

"Oh, dear. How can you tell that?" Big Bird wanted to know.

"From his footprints," Sherlock Hemlock told him. "They're enormous. Only someone very, very big could make footprints like that. Now, let us follow them and see where they lead."

Big Bird and Sherlock Hemlock followed the mysterious footprints, which led straight to Oscar's trash can. Big Bird knocked on the lid, and Oscar peeked out. "What do you want now?" he said.

"We're looking for the Mud Puddle Monster," said Big Bird. "Have you seen him? He's great big, all covered with mud, and he's real mad."

"No, I haven't seen him," said Oscar. "But I'll help you look for him. If he's as nice as he sounds, I'll invite him home for dinner."

Big Bird and Sherlock Hemlock and Oscar then followed the footprints right down the street and into Mr. Hooper's store. They asked Cookie Monster and Prairie Dawn if they had seen the Mud Puddle Monster.

"He's great big," said Big Bird, "and all covered with mud, and he's real mad, and he probably has lots of teeth and a nose shaped like a doorknob."

Cookie Monster and Prairie Dawn shook their heads. "I've never heard of a Mud Puddle Monster," said Prairie Dawn. "And I know I've never seen one."

"But he came right into the store," Big Bird insisted.

"Well, we not see him," Cookie Monster said.

"Egad," said Sherlock Hemlock. "Another clue. The Mud Puddle Monster came right into the store and no one saw him. That can only mean one thing. The Mud Puddle Monster is invisible!"

"Oh, no!" said Big Bird, feeling more frightened than ever. "He's invisible! Now what do we do?"

Sherlock Hemlock looked at the footprints through his magnifying glass. "We must keep following the footprints," he said. "Come along. They go right back out of the store."

Cookie Monster and Prairie Dawn decided to come, too. Prairie Dawn hung up a sign that said, "Closed. Back soon—I hope." And they all set off together.

The tracks now led to Ernie and Bert's door. Big Bird suddenly realized something. "Hey! That Mud Puddle Monster went everywhere I did. I went to Oscar's can, Mr. Hooper's store, and Ernie and Bert's apartment, too!"

"Of course," said Sherlock Hemlock. "It is all beginning to add up. He was following you."

Big Bird didn't say anything, but he was as frightened as he'd ever been.

Then Sherlock Hemlock said, "Wait. Here's another clue. The Mud Puddle Monster is still inside Ernie and Bert's apartment. See? The footprints go in, but they don't come out!"

Big Bird knocked loudly on the door. Ernie opened it, and Big Bird said, "Ernie, Ernie, a monster is hiding in your apartment!"

"Oh, dear," said Ernie. "What kind of monster?"

"It's the Mud Puddle Monster," said Big Bird. He's great big and he's mad and he's all covered with mud."

"He has lots of teeth, too," added Prairie Dawn.

"And a nose like a doorknob," chimed in Cookie Monster.

"And ears like tennis shoes," Big Bird went on, getting more excited.

"You can't see him because he's invisible," Sherlock Hemlock reminded everyone.

"I want to invite him home for dinner!" shouted Oscar.

"This is terrible," said Ernie. "What are we going to do?" And with that, they all began talking at once. Soon Bert came to the door to find out what was going on.

Big Bird pointed to the muddy footprints. "Look, Bert," he said. "Those muddy footprints go into your apartment, and they don't come out again."

"Of course they don't come out again," said Bert. "All the mud came off on our carpet. I've just been cleaning it up. Next time you come to visit us, Big Bird, I wish you would wipe your feet."

"Me?" said Big Bird. "Why? What did I do?"

"I just told you," said Bert. "You got mud all over our carpet when you came to see our new tablecloth. Those are *your* footprints."

"*My* footprints?" Big Bird looked down at his feet. Sure enough, his feet and the footprints were the same size and shape.

Sherlock Hemlock also looked at Big Bird's feet. Then he announced, "Aha! The final clue. I have solved the mystery!" He turned to Big Bird and said, "*You* are the Mysterious Mud Puddle Monster."

"Who?" said Big Bird. "Me?"

"Yes," said Sherlock Hemlock. "I, Sherlock Hemlock, the world's greatest detective, have piled clue upon clue, sifted all the evidence, and arrived with astounding swiftness at the conclusion to another baffling mystery. *You* are the Mud Puddle Monster."

"Oh, dear," thought Big Bird. "How silly. *I'm* not the Mud Puddle Monster. Why, there's probably no such thing as a Mud Puddle Monster." But he didn't tell Sherlock Hemlock that. "After all," he said to himself, "even the world's greatest detective makes mistakes."

"Well," said Sherlock Hemlock, "I must be going now. My job here is finished. Don't thank me. It's all in a day's work." Then he waved good-bye to everyone, turned, and went off, looking about him through his magnifying glass for his next case.

"Phooey," said Oscar. "Some Mud Puddle Monster. I'm going home."

"I'm just glad everything is all right after all," said Prairie Dawn. "Now I can go back to minding Mr. Hooper's store."

"Me come with you, Prairie Dawn," said Cookie Monster. "All the excitement make me hungry."

"Boy," said Ernie. "I think I feel like reading a nice un-scary story with no monsters. What do you say, Bert?"

Bert said he thought that was a good idea.

Big Bird, who was very happy to know he wasn't being followed by a big, angry, muddy monster with a nose like a doorknob, decided to take a nap. "Solving mysteries always makes me sleepy," he said.

4 and 15 Blackbirds

Count the blackbirds. This is the number **19**.
Find the blackbird wearing a **19**.

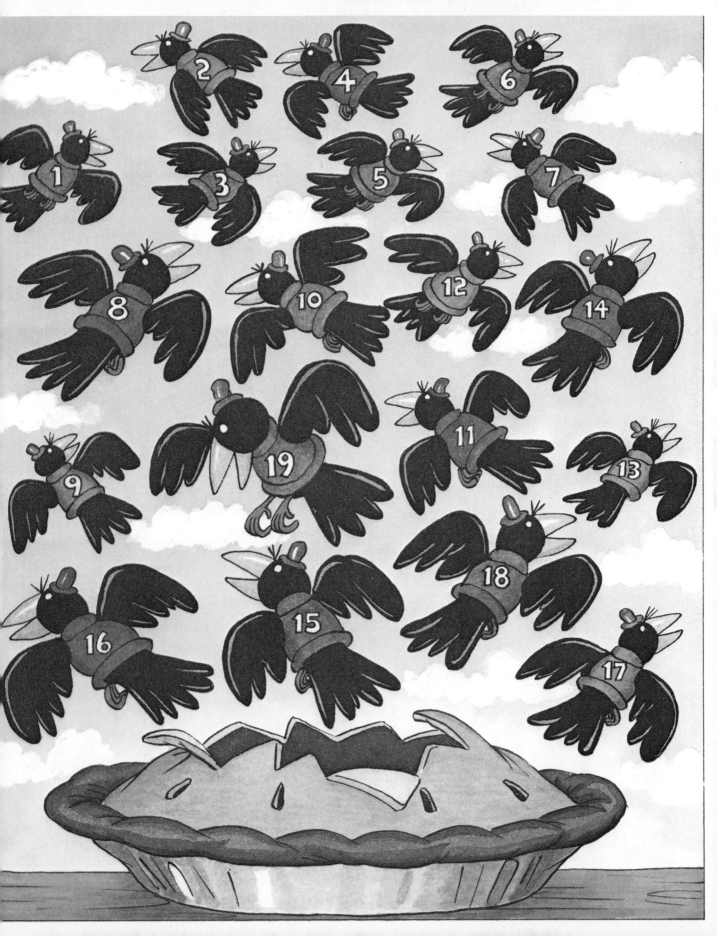

Find the Letters A to Z

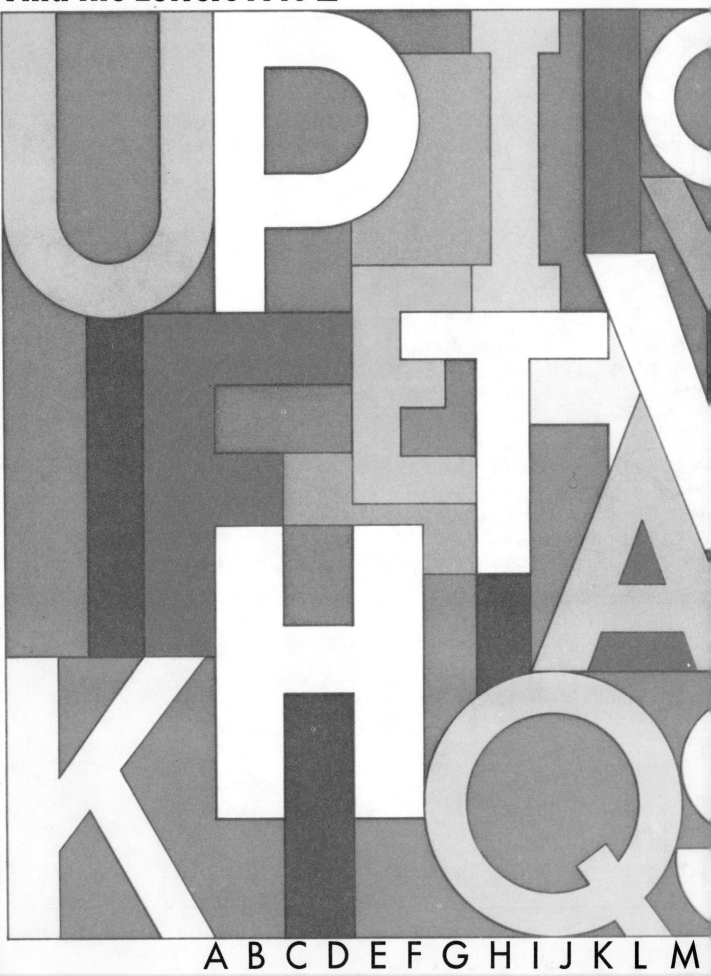

A B C D E F G H I J K L M

N O P Q R S T U V W X Y Z

Fun From Four to One

Big Bird, Cookie Monster and Grover were waiting to get into the circus. "When we get inside, let's get peanuts," Big Bird said. "Then let's try to find seats in the front row."

But there were lots of people waiting to get peanuts. If Big Bird, Cookie Monster and Grover waited in line for peanuts, there wouldn't be any front row seats left. "I have an idea," said Big Bird. "Two of us can go save seats. The other one can buy the peanuts."

"That good idea!" Cookie said. "That what me call *cooperation.* Big Bird and Grover go save seats. Me love peanuts. Me buy three bags of peanuts—one for Big Bird, one for Grover and one for me."

They all liked Cookie's idea. "But remember, Cookie," Big Bird warned, "don't eat the peanuts!"

Big Bird and Grover ran down to the first row and got three seats. Big Bird sat in one seat; Grover sat in another seat; and they saved a seat for Cookie Monster.

Meanwhile, Cookie Monster bought three bags of peanuts. He was heading for the front row when he tripped over someone's foot and fell. One bag of pea-nuts spilled on the floor—two bags of peanuts were left.

Cookie Monster started again for the first row. But he didn't watch where he was going, and he ran right into a clown. One bag of peanuts spilled on the floor—only one bag was left.

Cookie Monster finally got to the front row and sat down next to his friends. He gave each of them an empty bag.

"Hey, Cookie, I told you not to eat the peanuts!" Big Bird said.

"Me no eat peanuts," Cookie explained. "Me fall and one bag spilled on floor. Then me ran into clown and another bag spilled. Me have only one bag of peanuts left...my bag!"

"Wait a minute, Cookie," Grover said. "You are not cooperating. How do you know that that bag of peanuts is your bag? We can share that bag of peanuts."

"That good idea!" said Cookie Monster. "That what me call *cooperation!*"

As the band began to play and the ring-master came into the center ring, Big Bird, Cookie Monster and Grover shared the peanuts and watched the circus from the front row.

Let's Eat

Whose lunch boxes
are these?

It's Sam the Robot!

Where is Grover going?

Guess what! I'm going to school today!
My very first time. Oh, what will I say?
"Hello, my name's Grover. And how do you do?
Will you play with me if I play with you?"
Oh, that is quite nice—it's just what I'll say
When I meet my first friend at school today.
Good-bye to my mommy. Good-bye to my dad.
My first day of school…and Grover is glad!

What do **you** say when you meet a new friend?

Lawrence DiFiori

Happy Birthday, Dear ?

Hurray! There's a party on Sesame Street! With lots of balloons and good things to eat. It's time for the party! Can't wait anymore! But, hold on a minute—just whom is it for?

Not Ernie, not Bert, not Oscar, not Grover . . . So look very carefully, who is left over? He's friendly, he's furry, he's big and he's blue. He loves to eat cookies . . . now can you guess who?

After the Ball is Over

Here are two pictures in Cookie's house. Which one shows how the room looked **before** the party? Which one shows how it looked **after** the party?

How do you think Cookie Monster felt **before** the party? How do you think he felt **after** the party?

COOKIE

Happy Birthday

R.D

Which of These Things Belong Together?

What rhymes with cake?

What rhymes with sock?

What rhymes with jar?

Why is a dog's nose wet?

One day I was petting a dog friend of mine on the head.
The dog licked my hand. His nose touched my hand.
His nose was all wet!
Why was the dog's nose wet?
People's noses get wet sometimes when they have colds.
Did the dog have a cold?
No! Dogs are different than people.
When dogs have wet noses,
it doesn't mean that they have colds.
When dogs have wet noses, they are sweating.
When you feel hot, your body
has a way of making you feel cooler.
Your skin gets all wet. You sweat!
Dogs with wet noses are just trying to keep cool!

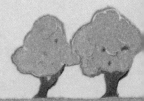

The Count's Counting Page

I'll tell you a secret. Don't laugh—it's no joke.
6 wonderful colors are inside my cloak!
I open my cloak—Ha! Ha! Ha!—A surprise!
6 marvelous colors to dazzle your eyes!
1, I count yellow. **2**, I count blue.
3, I count green. Are you counting too?
4, I count orange. **5**, I count pink.
6, I count **purple**. Now, what do you think?
I've told you my secret. You know it's no joke.
Oh, count all the colors you see in my cloak!

Can you find 15 Twiddlebugs?